SCHOLASTIC

Grammar, Reading & Maths 10-Minute Tests

Ages 5–6

10-Minute Tests

KS1 Year 1

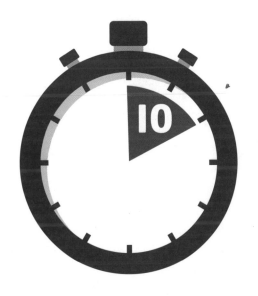

Track progress with
10-minute skills checks

Published in the UK by Scholastic, 2019

Scholastic Distribution Centre, Bosworth Avenue, Tournament Fields, Warwick, CV34 6UQ

Scholastic Ireland, 89E Lagan Road, Dublin Industrial Estate, Glasnevin, Dublin, D11 HP5F

SCHOLASTIC and associated logos are trademarks and/or registered trademarks of Scholastic Inc.

© 2019, Scholastic

2 3 4 5 6 7 8 9   3 4 5 6 7 8 9 0 1 2

A CIP catalogue record for this book is available from the British Library.

ISBN 978-1407-18312-1

Printed and bound by Ashford Colour Press Ltd, Gosport, Hampshire, PO13 0FW
Paper made from wood grown in sustainable forests and other controlled sources.

Authors

Grammar, Punctuation and Spelling: Shelley Welsh

Reading: Helen Betts and Wendy Joliffe

Maths: Paul Hollin

Editorial

Rachel Morgan, Audrey Stokes, Suzanne Adams, Kate Pedlar, Kate Baxter, Julia Roberts

Design

Nicolle Thomas, Neil Salt, Dan Prescott/Couper Street Type Co. and
Jayne Rawlings/Oxford Raw Design

Cover Illustration

Tania Bondar

Illustrations

grammar, reading and maths tests: Cathy Hughes; phonics checks: Jim Peacock

Technical artwork

Darren Lingard/D'Avila Illustration Agency

Photographs

page 36: polar bear, outdoorsman/Shutterstock; page 37: bathing polar bears, andamanec/
Shutterstock; page 38: blue whale, Maria Spb/Shutterstock; page 39: krill, Tarpan/Shutterstock

Contents

10 MINS

How to use this book

This book contains three grammar, punctuation and spelling tests, two phonics checks, two reading tests and two sets of maths tests for Year 1. The tests provide a wide coverage of the national curriculum for this age group. Guidance is given below for how long each test or set of tests should take to complete. However, timings at this age are not strict, so allow your child as much time as they need.

Grammar, punctuation and spelling

It is intended that children will take around ten minutes to complete each part of each test (ten minutes for grammar and punctuation, and ten minutes for spelling).

Grammar and punctuation tests

Each test comprises nine or ten questions, which amount to ten marks in total. Some questions require a selected response, where children select the correct answer from a list. Other questions require a constructed response, where children insert a word or punctuation mark, or write a short answer of their own.

Spelling tests

There are ten questions in each test, which amount to ten marks. Read each spelling number followed by *The word is...* Read the context sentence and then repeat *The word is...* Leave at least a 12-second gap between spellings. More information can be found on page 61.

Phonics Checks

The phonics checks provide practice for the National Phonics Screening Check that children complete towards the end of Year 1. These checks are designed to test a child's knowledge of phonics and require children to read single words aloud. More information on these checks can be found on page 6.

Reading

Each test comprises a short piece of text followed by comprehension questions. It is intended that children will take around ten minutes to complete each test. Some questions require a selected response, where children choose the correct answer from several options. Other questions require a constructed response, where children write a short or extended answer of their own.

Maths

It is intended that children will take around ten minutes to complete each set of two tests. Some questions require a selected response, for example where children choose the correct answer from several options. Other questions require a constructed response, where children work out and write down their own answer.

Marking the tests

A mark scheme and a progress chart are included towards the end of this book. After your child has completed a test, mark it and together identify and practise any areas where your child is less confident.

Phonics checks guidance

The phonics screening checks on pages 22 to 31 are designed to test a child's knowledge of phonics as one of the building blocks in learning to read and spell. For this purpose, pseudo-words (nonsense words) are used, as a child has to rely on his or her phonic knowledge to read them.

Complete each phonics screening check individually with your child. Introduce the check, as follows:

- I am going to ask you to read some words out loud.

- Some of these words will be new and some you will have seen before.

- Some of the words are not real words but names of imaginary creatures. There is a picture of the creature next to it.

- I will tell you each time you read words that are not real.

Point to each word in turn, for your child to read out loud. Record your child's response to each word, noting if they say it correctly or incorrectly, with comments against incorrect answers; for example, note if your child reads some sounds in the word correctly, but not all, or if your child tries to give a real word instead of a nonsense word. During the phonics check, point to whole words, but do not point in a way that supports the decoding of the word. For example, do not point to individual letters or groups of letters such as 'g' or 'sh'.

Guidance on how to mark the checks can be found on page 55–56.

Grammar and Punctuation
Test 1

10 MINS

1. Circle **one** word in the sentence below that describes the dog.

Jilly   stroked   the   little   dog.

2. Write the **plural** of the words below on the line next to each one.

One has been done for you.

One boy	Two *boys*
A kiss	Some _____
One witch	Those _____

3. Tick the name of the **punctuation mark** that comes at the end of each sentence.

Sentence	Full stop	Question mark	Exclamation mark
How fabulous the weather is today!			
We are going to the beach later.			
Would you like to come with us?			

Marks

1

1

1

7

Marks

4. Add the **two** missing **full stops** to the sentences below.

We take the bus to school Sometimes Dad drives us there in the car

1

5. Circle **two** words in the sentence below that should start with a **capital letter**.

my friend lives in london.

1

6. Tick the correct ending for the word <u>quick</u> to complete the sentence.

Rahul was the quick_____ runner in the class.

Tick **one**.

er ☐

ing ☐

est ☐

ly ☐

1

Marks

7. Tick the word that completes the sentence below.

Bashir _____ Freddie are playing in the garden.

Tick **one**.

but ☐

if ☐

and ☐

or ☐

1

8. Which **punctuation mark** is needed at the end of the sentence below?

It's very cold today, isn't it

Tick **one**.

an exclamation mark ☐

a question mark ☐

a full stop ☐

an apostrophe ☐

1

KEEP IT GOING!

Marks

9. Tick **two** words in the sentence below that tell you what Freya <u>did</u>.

Freya took off her coat and hung it on the hook

↑   ↑   ↑

☐   ☐   ☐

behind the door.

↑

☐

2

KEEP IT GOING!

Well done! END OF GRAMMAR & PUNCTUATION TEST 1!

Spelling
Test 1

Marks

1. I _____ two sisters.

2. The stone _____ to the bottom of the lake.

3. Raj is going to _____ in Spain.

4. Mum and I tidied my _____.

5. Pilar is _____ than Gemma.

6. The cat _____ under the chair.

7. Dad made a _____ sauce to go with the meal.

8. Flo came _____ in the running race.

9. The _____ was my favourite animal in the zoo.

10. I played a _____ on the piano.

10

Well done! END OF SPELLING TEST 1!

Grammar and Punctuation
Test 2

10 MINS

Marks

1. Which word in the sentence below tells you <u>how</u> Jack was playing with his toys?

Jack was playing quietly with his toys.

Tick one.

his	☐
quietly	☐
with	☐
was	☐

1

2. What is the name of the **punctuation mark** at the end of the sentence below?

How beautiful the weather is today!

Tick one.

a question mark	☐
an exclamation mark	☐
a full stop	☐
a comma	☐

1

10 MINS

Marks

3. Finish the word that is the opposite of <u>kind</u> by choosing the correct **prefix** and writing it on the line.

| no | re | un |

_____kind

1

4. Circle **two** words in the sentence below that should start with a **capital letter**.

the   teacher   said   i   had   worked   very   hard.

1

5. Circle **one** word that describes Alfie in the sentence below.

Alfie   was   tired   after   his   long   walk.

1

6. Insert **one** word to join the two parts of the sentence.

Maya plays cricket _____ Rajiv plays tennis.

1

10 MINS

Marks

7. How do you know the sentence below is a **question**?

What time do you go to bed?

Tick **one**.

It ends with a question mark. ☐

It starts with a capital letter. ☐

It ends with a full stop. ☐

It ends with an exclamation mark. ☐

1

8. Tick **one** word in the sentence below that tells you what Jack is doing.

Jack draws a picture.

☐ ☐ ☐

1

KEEP IT GOING!

Marks

9. Finish the sentence by choosing the correct **ending** for the word <u>jump</u> and writing it on the line.

Keir was jump_____ on his bed.

1

10. Draw lines to pairs of words to make **three** longer words.
One has been done for you.

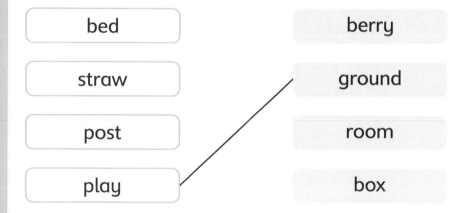

bed	berry
straw	ground
post	room
play	box

1

Well done! END OF GRAMMAR &
PUNCTUATION TEST 2!

15

Spelling

Marks

1. Dad showed me _____ he works.

2. Rita put the rabbit back in the _____.

3. There was a beautiful _____ last night.

4. Sinead forgot her football _____.

5. Our cousins are _____ with us.

6. Everyone in my _____ likes pizza.

7. I didn't have a _____ about my birthday surprise.

8. There is a hole in my coat _____.

9. The cat jumped _____ the wall.

10. Beth can run fast but Ushma is _____.

10

Well done! END OF SPELLING TEST 2!

Grammar and Punctuation
Test 3

10 MINS

Marks

1. Choose the correct word from the box to complete the sentence. Write it on the line.

or	but	and

Faisal likes both chocolate _____ vanilla ice cream.

1

2. Circle **two** words in the sentence below that describe the weather.

"Today it will be warm and sunny," said Dad with a smile.

1

3. Add the missing **punctuation mark** to the sentence in the speech bubble below.

Can you come to my party

1

17

10 MINS

Marks

4. What is the name of the **punctuation mark** at the end of the sentence below?

What a surprise it is to see you again!

Tick **one**.

a question mark ☐

a comma ☐

an exclamation mark ☐

a full stop ☐

1

5. Circle **two** words in the sentence below that should start with a **capital letter**.

on   saturday   mornings,   we   go   swimming.

1

6. Finish the sentence by choosing the correct **prefix** and writing it on the line to show that Billy was taking his shoes off.

| de | un | re |

Billy _____tied his shoe laces.

1

10 MINS

Marks

7. Write out the words in the boxes to make **one** sentence.

Write your sentence on the lines.

Remember to punctuate your sentence correctly.

| in the park. | went for a walk | Will and Sara |

_____

_____

_____

1

8. Circle **one** word in the sentence below that tells you what Mum is <u>doing</u>.

Mum   chops   the   apple   into   small   pieces.

1

KEEP IT GOING!

19

9. Tick the sentence below that is correctly punctuated.

Tick **one**.

We are going on holiday to spain next week.	☐
We are going on holiday to Spain next week	☐
we are going on holiday to Spain next week.	☐
We are going on holiday to Spain next week.	☐

Marks

1

10. Tick the sentence that shows Jaime is asking for a glass of milk.

Tick **one**.

"Pour the milk carefully," said Jaime.	☐
"I like drinking milk," said Jaime.	☐
"What a lovely drink of milk that was!" said Jaime.	☐
"Please may I have a glass of milk?" said Jaime.	☐

1

Well done! END OF GRAMMAR & PUNCTUATION TEST 3!

Spelling
Test 3

Marks

1. I _____ I will play with my toys later.

2. Please give me my pencil _____.

3. Freya _____ TV before dinner.

4. Mum made a cheese _____ for lunch.

5. Dan _____ the ball to Finn.

6. Dad _____ his brother who lives in America.

7. Ella scored a _____ in PE.

8. I _____ my new shoes today.

9. That man is trying to _____ the cat.

10. We planted some seeds in the _____.

10

Well done! END OF SPELLING TEST 3!

Phonics
Check 1

Marks

1.

fod

1

2.

wep

1

3.

vam

1

4.

ust

1

5. | Marks

shap

1

6.

yick

1

7.

heek

1

8.

choin

1

Marks

9.

crun

1

10.

glith

1

11.

jebs

1

12.

wooks

1

13.

thud

1

14.

fizz

1

15.

corn

1

16.

chess

1

Marks

10 MINS

Marks

17.

clog

1

18.

spark

1

19.

quilt

1

20.

shaft

1

Marks

1.

zurm

1

2.

hobe

1

3.

zair

1

4.

floak

1

Marks

5.

grawns

1

6.

plost

1

7.

screve

1

8.

sploy

1

Marks

9.

herd

1

10.

whale

1

11.

thigh

1

12.

shrill

1

13.

flaunt

Marks

1

14.

thrift

1

15.

spray

1

16.

strap

1

Marks

17.

older

1

18.

chorus

1

19.

wailing

1

20.

graphite

1

Reading
Test 1

10 MINS

Goldilocks and the wolf

Goldilocks was a girl with golden hair.
She liked to pick flowers.
She had a basket to put them in.
She liked to visit the three bears.

A long time ago, she ate the bears' food.
She broke a chair and she slept in their beds.
The bears were very cross.

Marks

1. Why did Goldilocks have a basket?

_____

_____

1

2. Which of these things did Goldilocks do at the three bears' house?

Tick **one**.

She had a drink. ☐

She slept in their beds. ☐

She sat on the sofa. ☐

1

3. **Find** and **copy one** word that means the same as <u>angry</u>.

_____

1

10 MINS

One day, Goldilocks went to visit Red Riding Hood's grandma. The old lady lived in the woods. Goldilocks hoped she would get cake there.

4. Who did Goldilocks go to visit?

_____

_____

Marks

1

5. What did Goldilocks hope she might get there?

_____

1

33

On the way, Goldilocks picked flowers.
She saw something in the woods.
It was big. It was hairy. It had big ears.

Goldilocks ran to the old lady's house.
She banged on the door.
The old lady opened it. She looked odd.
She had a big mouth. She had big ears.
She had sharp teeth.

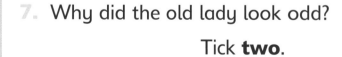

6. What animal do you think Goldilocks saw in the woods?

Marks

Tick **one**.

a mouse ☐

a wolf ☐

a deer ☐

1

7. Why did the old lady look odd?

Tick **two**.

She had a big mouth. ☐

She had a big nose. ☐

KEEP IT GOING!

She had sharp teeth. ☐

1

"Come in," said the old lady.

Goldilocks went inside.

"Have some cake," said the old lady.

Goldilocks saw that the old lady had sharp claws! This was not Red Riding Hood's gran. It was a wolf!

Goldilocks ran out of the door fast. She ran all the way home. She did not go into the woods again for a very long time. She did not want to see anyone with big ears!

8. Number the sentences 1–4 to show the order of the story.

Marks

Goldilocks ran out of the door fast.	
She did not go into the woods again.	
Goldilocks went inside the house.	
It was a wolf!	

1

9. Why did Goldilocks run all the way home?

_____

_____

2

Well done! END OF READING TEST 1!

35

Reading
Test 2

Amazing animals

Let's meet two of the world's biggest animals!

Polar bears live in the Arctic. It is cold there. They have thick fur to keep warm. They have fat under their skin. This is called blubber. It keeps them warm.

Marks

1. Where do polar bears live?

_____

1

2. **Find** and **copy one** word that tells you what a polar bear's fur is like.

_____

1

3. What does blubber protect polar bears from?

Tick **one**.

heat ☐   cold ☐   hunger ☐

1

Adult polar bears are very big. Baby polar bears are tiny. They are around the same size as a rabbit.

Polar bears are good swimmers. They have wide paws. They use them like paddles.

4. **Find** and **copy one** word which means the same as <u>very small</u>.

_____

Marks

1

5. What is a baby polar bear around the same size as? Circle the correct answer.

| a paddle | a rabbit | an adult's paws |

1

6. What do polar bears have that help them to swim well? Circle the correct answer.

| big babies | tiny ears | wide paws |

1

The blue whale is the biggest animal in the world. It can be as long as three buses. It can weigh more than three lorries.

Baby blue whales are very big too. They are as long as two cars.

7. Tick **true** or **false** for each sentence below.

Marks

	True	False
The blue whale is the smallest animal in the world.		
The blue whale can weigh more than three lorries.		
Baby blue whales are very small.		

1

8. What does this page tell you about a blue whale?

Tick **one**.

what it eats ☐   its size ☐   where it lives ☐

1

38

The blue whale eats tiny animals. They are called krill. A blue whale eats millions of krill every day.

9. What is the name of the animal that blue whales eat?

_____

Marks

1

10. Why does a blue whale need to eat millions of krill every day?

_____

_____

1

Maths
Set A Test 1: Arithmetic

10 MINS

1. $2 + 5 =$ [ ]

1

2. $16 - 6 =$ [ ]

1

3. $97 + 4 =$ [ ]

1

10 MINS

Marks

4. $11 - \boxed{} = 0$

1

5. $6 + 6 + 6 = \boxed{}$

1

6. $22 - 9 = \boxed{}$

1

Well done! END OF MATHS SET A TEST 1!

10 MINS

Marks

1. A boat is leaving a harbour.

It must turn to face the exit.

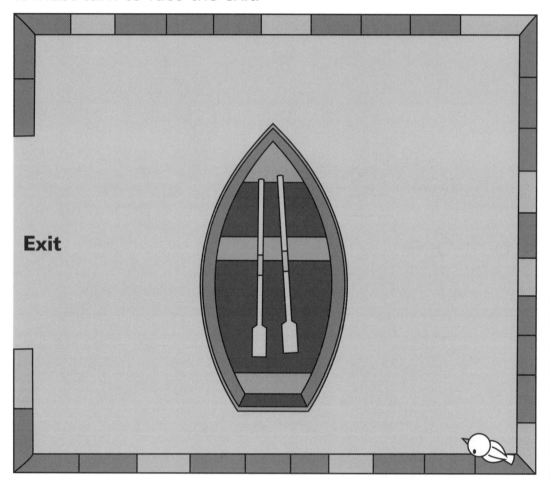

Exit

If it turns in an anti-clockwise direction, what size turn must the boat make?

Tick **one**.

quarter turn   half turn   three-quarter turn

1

Marks

2. Here is a set of triangles.

Draw a line to divide the set in half.

1

3. Measure these 5 pencils with a ruler.

Which pencil is 9cm long?

1

Write the letters of 3 pencils to make this statement true:

Pencil _____ is longer than pencil _____, but it is shorter than pencil _____.

1

Marks

4. Look at these numbers.

$$3 \quad 8 \quad 11 \quad 14 \quad 17$$

Use **three** of the numbers to complete this number sentence.

□ − □ = □

1

5. Khalid has 2 jars of marbles.

How many marbles does he have altogether?

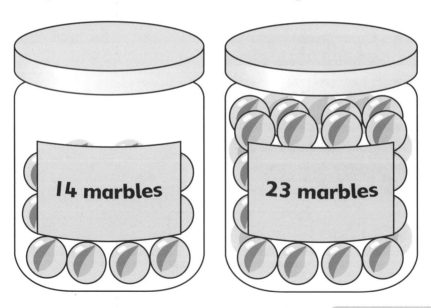

14 marbles

23 marbles

marbles

1

6. Hamish and Nora arrange pound coins in rows of 3.

If they make 5 rows of pound coins, how much money will they have?

pounds

1

Well done! END OF MATHS SET A TEST 2!

Maths

10 MINS

1. $8 - 7 = \boxed{}$

1

2. $64 - 1 = \boxed{}$

1

3. $10 + 10 + 10 + 10 = \boxed{}$

1

10 MINS

Marks

4. $104 - 5 = \boxed{}$

1

5. $12 + \boxed{} = 20$

1

6. $15 + 13 = \boxed{}$

Well done! END OF MATHS SET B TEST 1!

1

47

Maths
Set B Test 2: Reasoning

10 MINS

Marks

1. Tick each shape that has $\frac{1}{4}$ shaded.

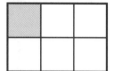

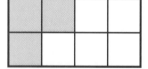

1

2. Here is a number line.

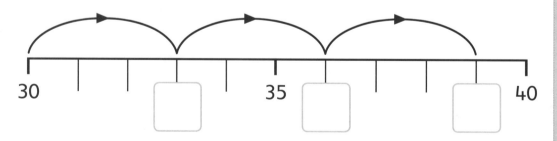

Zoe starts at 30 and counts in steps of 3.

Write the 3 numbers she lands on in the boxes.

1

Marks

3. Draw a line to match each 3D shape to its name.

 cylinder   pyramid   cuboid

1

4. Josh has some blocks.

He arranges them in 3 equal rows.

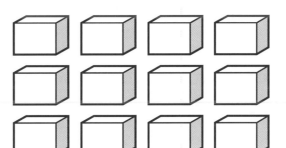

Leanne takes all of Josh's blocks and arranges them in 2 equal rows.

How many blocks will be in each row?

 blocks

1

Marks

5. Dina had lunch at this time.

She had an afternoon snack 3 hours later.

Draw clock hands on the clock below to show the time Dina had her afternoon snack.

1

10 MINS

Marks

6. 3 children stand in a line.

Their teacher measures the distances between them.

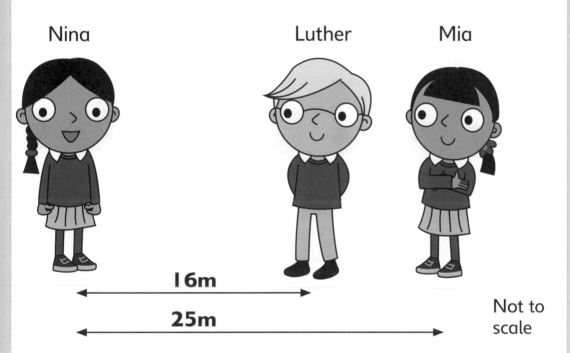

Nina   Luther   Mia

16m

25m

Not to scale

The distance from Nina to Luther is 16 metres.

The distance from Mia to Nina is 25 metres.

How far apart are Mia and Luther?

| | metres |

1

Well done! END OF MATHS SET B TEST 2!

51

Answers
Grammar and Punctuation

Q	Mark scheme for Grammar and Punctuation Test 1	Marks
1	**Award 1 mark** if 'little' is circled. **Grammar essentials:** An adjective can come before the noun, as here, to modify it, or after the verb 'to be' as its complement.	1
2	**Award 1 mark** for 'Some **kisses**' and 'Those **witches**'. **Grammar essentials:** Regular nouns add 's' or 'es' for plural form.	1
3	**Award 1 mark** for each row ticked correctly: *(table below)* **Grammar and punctuation essentials:** An exclamation sentence starts with 'How' or 'What', contains a verb and ends with an exclamation mark. A statement tells you something and ends with a full stop. A question is a sentence that asks something and ends with a question mark.	1
4	**Award 1 mark** for: 'We take the bus to school. Sometimes Dad drives us there in the car.' **Punctuation essentials:** A statement ends with a full stop.	1
5	**Award 1 mark** if 'my' and 'london' are circled. **Punctuation essentials:** A sentence starts with a capital letter. Names of places also start with a capital letter.	1
6	**Award 1 mark** if 'est' is ticked. **Grammar essentials:** The suffixes 'est', 'ed' and 'ing' can be added to some verbs and adjectives. Sometimes, we may need to change the spelling of the root word, for example: happy, happiest.	1
7	**Award 1 mark** if 'and' is ticked. **Grammar essentials:** The word 'and' is a co-ordinating conjunction used to join words and clauses.	1
8	**Award 1 mark** if 'a question mark' is ticked. **Grammar and punctuation essentials:** A question is a sentence that asks something. It starts with a capital letter and ends with a question mark.	1
9	**Award 2 marks** if both 'took' and 'hung' are ticked. **Award 1 mark** for one correct answer. **Grammar essentials:** A verb is a word that names an action, a state of being or a feeling.	2
	Total	10

Question 3 table:

Sentence	Full stop	Question mark	Exclamation mark
How fabulous the weather is today!			✔
We are going to the beach later.	✔		
Would you like to come with us?		✔	

Q	Mark scheme for Grammar and Punctuation Test 2	Marks
1	**Award 1 mark** if 'quietly' is ticked. **Grammar essentials:** An adverb can give more information about the verb in a sentence.	1
2	**Award 1 mark** if 'an exclamation mark' is ticked. **Grammar and punctuation essentials:** An exclamation sentence starts with 'How' or 'What', contains a verb and ends with an exclamation mark.	1
3	**Award 1 mark** for the addition of 'un' to form '**un**kind'. **Grammar essentials:** The prefix 'un' changes the meaning of adjectives, adverbs and verbs.	1
4	**Award 1 mark** if 'the' and 'i' are circled. **Punctuation essentials:** A sentence starts with a capital letter and the pronoun 'I' is always written with the capital letter 'I'.	1
5	**Award 1 mark** if 'tired' is circled. **Grammar essentials:** An adjective can come before the noun, to modify it, or after the verb 'to be', as here, as its complement.	1
6	**Award 1 mark** if the word 'and' or 'but' is inserted. Also accept 'while' or 'when'. **Grammar essentials:** The words 'and' and 'but' are co-ordinating conjunctions used to join words and clauses. The words 'while' and 'when' are subordinating conjunctions, which are used to join subordinate clauses to main clauses.	1
7	**Award 1 mark** if 'It ends with a question mark.' is ticked. **Punctuation essentials:** A question is a sentence that asks something. It starts with a capital letter and ends with a question mark.	1
8	**Award 1 mark** if 'draws' is ticked. **Grammar essentials:** A verb is a word that names an action, a state of being or a feeling.	1
9	**Award 1 mark** if the suffix 'ing' has been added to form 'jump**ing**'. **Grammar essentials:** The suffix 'ing' can be added to some verbs without needing to change the spelling of the root word.	1
10	**Award 1 mark** for all three correct: bedroom, stawberry, postbox. **Grammar essentials:** Compound words are two words joined together to make a new word.	1
	Total	10

Q	Mark scheme for Grammar and Punctuation Test 3	Marks
1	**Award 1 mark** if the word 'and' has been inserted. **Grammar essentials:** The word 'and' is a co-ordinating conjunction that can be used to join words or clauses.	1
2	**Award 1 mark** if both 'warm' and 'sunny' are circled. **Grammar essentials:** An adjective can come before the noun, to modify it, or after the verb 'to be', as here, as its complement.	1
3	**Award 1 mark** if a question mark has been added to the end of the sentence. **Punctuation essentials:** A question is a sentence that asks something. It starts with a capital letter and ends with a question mark.	1
4	**Award 1 mark** if 'an exclamation mark' is ticked. **Punctuation essentials:** An exclamation sentence starts with 'How' or 'What', contains a verb and ends with an exclamation mark.	1
5	**Award 1 mark** if both 'on' and 'saturday' are circled. **Punctuation essentials:** A sentence starts with a capital letter and the days of the week and names of people start with a capital letter.	1
6	**Award 1 mark** for the addition of 'un' to form '**un**tied'. **Grammar essentials:** The prefix 'un' changes the meaning of adjectives, adverbs and verbs.	1
7	**Award 1 mark** for: 'Will and Sara went for a walk in the park.' **Punctuation essentials:** A statement starts with a capital letter and ends with a full stop.	1
8	**Award 1 mark** if 'chops' is circled. **Grammar essentials:** A verb is a word that names an action, a state of being or a feeling.	1
9	**Award 1 mark** if 'We are going on holiday to Spain next week.' is ticked. **Punctuation essentials:** A statement starts with a capital letter and ends with a full stop. The name of a place, such as Spain, starts with a capital letter.	1
10	**Award 1 mark** if '"Please may I have a glass of milk?" said Jaime.' is ticked. **Punctuation essentials:** A question is a sentence that asks something. It starts with a capital letter and ends with a question mark.	1
	Total	10

Phonics checks guidance

Marking the check

The following key points should be remembered when scoring the check.
Score one mark for each correct word read.

- Children may sound out parts of the word before reading the whole word, but this is optional.

- Children may stretch the phonemes (single letter sounds, or combination of letter sounds) but as long as they blend correctly to pronounce the word, a mark may be awarded.

- Alternative pronunciations should be considered for pseudo-words if the sounds exist in other words, for example: a soft 'g' or hard 'g' sound in 'ged' – see further guidance on page 56.

- A child's accent should be taken into account and not disadvantage him or her. Similarly, if a child has particular speech difficulties, for example, in pronouncing 'th', this should be taken into account.

- If a child makes an incorrect attempt but then corrects it, this should be marked as correct.

In the National Phonics Screening Check, there are two sections. Section 2 has more complex words than Section 1. The full check has 40 words across the two sections and children need to read at least 32 words correctly.

In this book, each check contains 20 words and so children should be achieving around 16 words per check. However, Check 1 is similar to Section 1 of the national check and Check 2 is more similar to Section 2 (the harder part).

Therefore, it is likely that your child will find Check 1 easier and so may score higher in this than in Check 2. The target of 16 should be treated as a rough guide only; if you have any concerns, please speak to your child's teacher.

10 MINS

Check 1

Score one mark for each correct word read.

Pseudo words	Acceptable pronunciations	Real words
1. fod	This item uses the 'f' from 'fib' and rhymes with 'nod'.	13. thud
2. wep	This item uses the 'w' from 'web' and rhymes with 'step'.	14. fizz
3. vam	This item uses the 'v' from 'van' and rhymes with 'ham'.	15. corn
4. ust	This item uses the 'u' from 'under' and rhymes with 'must'.	16. chess
5. shap	This item uses the 'sh' from 'shop' and rhymes with 'clap'.	17. clog
6. yick	This item uses the 'y' from 'you' and rhymes with 'pick'.	18. spark
7. heek	This item uses the 'h' from 'head' and rhymes with 'peek'.	19. quilt
8. choin	This item uses the 'ch' from 'chip' and rhymes with 'coin'.	20. shaft
9. crun	This item uses the 'cr' from 'crib' and rhymes with 'run'.	
10. glith	This item uses the 'gl' from 'glad' and rhymes with 'pith'.	
11. jebs	This item uses the 'j' from 'jet' and rhymes with 'webs'.	
12. wooks	This item uses the 'w' from 'web' and rhymes with 'spooks' or 'books'.	

Check 2

Score one mark for each correct word read.

Pseudo words	Acceptable pronunciations	Real words
1. zurm	This item uses the 'z' from 'zip' and rhymes with 'worm'.	9. herd
2. hobe	This item uses the 'h' from 'hot' and rhymes with 'robe'.	10. whale
3. zair	This item uses the 'z' from 'zip' and rhymes with 'hair'.	11. thigh
4. floak	This item uses the 'fl' from 'fly' and rhymes with 'cloak'.	12. shrill
5. grawns	This item uses the 'gr' from 'grow' and rhymes with 'prawns'.	13. flaunt
6. plost	This item uses the 'pl' from 'play' and rhymes with 'frost'.	14. thrift
7. screve	This item uses the 'scr' from 'scrap' and rhymes with 'leave'.	15. spray
8. sploy	This item uses the 'spl' from 'splat' and rhymes with 'toy'.	16. strap
		17. older
		18. chorus
		19. wailing
		20. graphite

Answers
Reading

Q	Mark scheme for Reading Test 1: Goldilocks and the wolf	Marks
1	**Award 1 mark** for: for flowers/to put flowers in	1
2	**Award 1 mark** for: She slept in their beds.	1
3	**Award 1 mark** for: cross	1
4	**Award 1 mark** for: an old lady/Red Riding Hood's grandma	1
5	**Award 1 mark** for: cake	1
6	**Award 1 mark** for: a wolf	1
7	**Award 1 mark** for both: She had a big mouth. and She had sharp teeth.	1
8	**Award 1 mark** for all four sentences in the correct order:	1

Goldilocks ran out of the door fast.	3
She did not go into the woods again.	4
Goldilocks went inside the house.	1
It was a wolf!	2

Q		Marks
9	**Award 2 marks** for an answer such as: She was running away from the wolf. OR She was too scared to stop in case the wolf caught her. **Award 1 mark** for an answer which suggests she is scared but which does not mention the wolf.	2
	Total	10

Q	Mark scheme for Reading Test 2: Amazing animals	Marks
1	**Award 1 mark** for: (in the) Arctic Do not accept more general references to cold places, for example 'somewhere cold'.	1
2	**Award 1 mark** for: thick	1
3	**Award 1 mark** for: cold	1
4	**Award 1 mark** for: tiny	1
5	**Award 1 mark** for: a rabbit	1
6	**Award 1 mark** for: wide paws	1
7	**Award 1 mark** for all answers correct:	1

	True	False
The blue whale is the smallest animal in the world.		✔
The blue whale can weigh more than three lorries.	✔	
Baby blue whales are very small.		✔

Q		Marks
8	**Award 1 mark** for: its size	1
9	**Award 1 mark** for: krill	1
10	**Award 1 mark** for: references to krill being tiny and the whale being big, or references to it taking a lot of krill to fill it up. Do not allow references to the whale being greedy.	1
	Total	10

Answers

Maths

Q	Mark scheme for Maths Set A Test 1 – Arithmetic	Marks
1	7	1
2	10	1
3	101	1
4	11	1
5	18	1
6	13	1
	Total	**6**

Q	Mark scheme for Maths Set A Test 2 – Reasoning	Marks
1	quarter turn	1
2	Other ways of drawing the dividing line are possible.	1
3	D	1
	Several answers are possible, such as: *Pencil A is longer than pencil B, but shorter than pencil C.*	1
4	11 – 3 = 8, 11 – 8 = 3, 14 – 3 = 11, 14 – 11 = 3, 17 – 3 = 14 or 17 – 14 = 3	1
5	37 marbles	1
6	15 pounds	1
	Total	**7**

Q	Mark scheme for Maths Set B Test 1 – Arithmetic	Marks
1	1	1
2	63	1
3	40	1
4	99	1
5	8	1
6	28	1
	Total	**6**

Q	Mark scheme for Maths Set B Test 2 – Reasoning	Marks
1		1
2	33, 36, 39	1

59

Q	Mark scheme for Maths Set B Test 2 – Reasoning continued	Marks
3	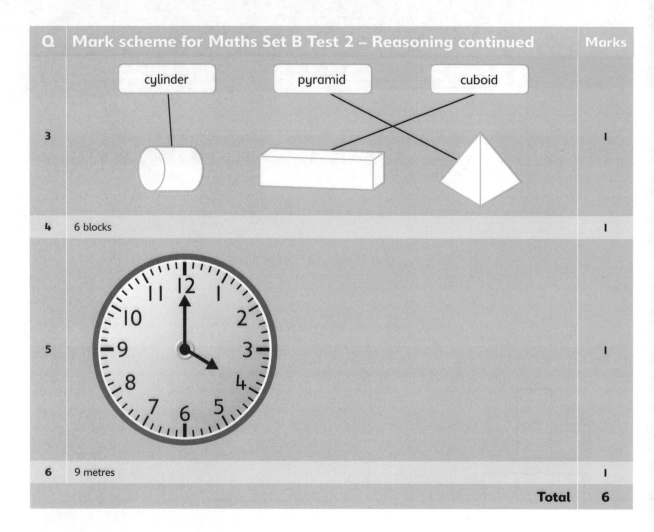	1
4	6 blocks	1
5		1
6	9 metres	1
	Total	6

How to administer the spelling tests

10 MINS

There are three short spelling tests in this book. Each test consists of ten questions; you should allow your child as much time as they need to complete them.

Read the instructions in the box below.

> *Listen carefully to the instructions I am going to give you.*
>
> *I am going to read ten sentences to you. Each sentence on your answer sheet has a missing word. Listen carefully to the missing word and write it in the space provided, making sure you spell the word correctly. I will read the word, then the word within the sentence, then repeat the word a third time.*
>
> *Do you have any questions?*

Read the spellings as follows:

- Give the question number, 'Spelling 1'
- Say, 'The word is...'
- Read the whole sentence to show the word in context
- Repeat, 'The word is...'

Leave at least a 12-second gap between each spelling.

At the end re-read all ten questions. Then say, 'This is the end of the test. Please put down your pencil or pen.'

Each correct answer should be awarded **1 mark**.

Spelling test transcripts

Spelling test 1

Spelling 1: The word is **have**.
I **have** two sisters.
The word is **have**.

Spelling 2: The word is **sank**.
The stone **sank** to the bottom of the lake.
The word is **sank**.

Spelling 3: The word is **live**.
Raj is going to **live** in Spain.
The word is **live**.

Spelling 4: The word is **bedroom**.
Mum and I tidied my **bedroom**.
The word is **bedroom**.

Spelling 5: The word is **older**.
Pilar is **older** than Gemma.
The word is **older**.

Spelling 6: The word is **crawled**.
The cat **crawled** under the chair.
The word is **crawled**.

Spelling 7: The word is **rich**.
Dad made a **rich** sauce to go with the meal.
The word is **rich**.

Spelling 8: The word is **third**.
Flo came **third** in the running race.
The word is **third**.

Spelling 9: The word is **elephant**.
The **elephant** was my favourite animal in the zoo.
The word is **elephant**.

Spelling 10: The word is **tune**.
I played a **tune** on the piano.
The word is **tune**.

Spelling test 2

Spelling 1: The word is **where**.
Dad showed me **where** he works.
The word is **where**.

Spelling 2: The word is **hutch**.
Rita put the rabbit back in the **hutch**.
The word is **hutch**.

Spelling 3: The word is **sunset**.
There was a beautiful **sunset** last night.
The word is **sunset**.

Spelling 4: The word is **kit**.
Sinead forgot her football **kit**.
The word is **kit**.

Spelling 5: The word is **staying**.
Our cousins are **staying** with us.
The word is **staying**.

Spelling 6: The word is **family**.
Everyone in my **family** likes pizza.
The word is **family**.

Spelling 7: The word is **clue**.
I didn't have a **clue** about my birthday surprise.
The word is **clue**.

Spelling 8: The word is **pocket**.
There is a hole in my coat **pocket**.
The word is **pocket**.

Spelling 9: The word is **off**.
The cat jumped **off** the wall.
The word is **off**.

Spelling 10: The word is **quicker**.
Beth can run fast but Ushma is **quicker**.
The word is **quicker**.

Spelling test 3

Spelling 1: The word is **think**.
I **think** I will play with my toys later.
The word is **think**.

Spelling 2: The word is **back**.
Please give me my pencil **back**.
The word is **back**.

Spelling 3: The word is **watches**.
Freya **watches** TV before dinner.
The word is **watches**.

Spelling 4: The word is **pie**.
Mum made a cheese **pie** for lunch.
The word is **pie**.

Spelling 5: The word is **threw**.
Dan **threw** the ball to Finn.
The word is **threw**.

Spelling 6: The word is **misses**.
Dad **misses** his brother who lives in America.
The word is **misses**.

Spelling 7: The word is **goal**.
Ella scored a **goal** in PE.
The word is **goal**.

Spelling 8: The word is **wore**.
I **wore** my new shoes today.
The word is **wore**.

Spelling 9: The word is **rescue**.
That man is trying to **rescue** the cat.
The word is **rescue**.

Spelling 10: The word is **soil**.
We planted some seeds in the **soil**.
The word is **soil**.

Progress chart

Fill in your score in the table below to see how well you've done.

Test number	Score	Percentage		Percentage	
Grammar, Punctuation and Spelling Test 1	/20				Good try! You need more practice in some topics – ask an adult to help you.
Grammar, Punctuation and Spelling Test 2	/20			0–33%	
Grammar, Punctuation and Spelling Test 3	/20				
Phonics Check 1	/20				You're doing really well. Ask for extra help for any topics you found tricky.
Phonics Check 2	/20			34–69%	
Reading Test 1	/10				
Reading Test 2	/10			70–100%	You're a 10-Minute SATs Test star – good work!
Maths Set A: Test 1	/13				
Maths Set A: Test 2					
Maths Set B: Test 1	/12				
Maths Set B: Test 2					

Reward Certificate

Well done!

You have completed all of the 10-Minute Tests

Name: _____   Date: _____

SCHOLASTIC

You've taken your 10-minute tests...
now try a complete practice paper

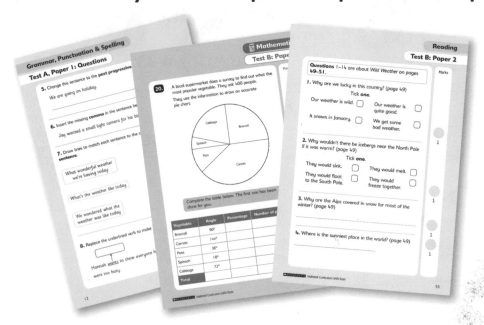

Ages 6–7
Year 2

Ages 7–8
Year 3

Ages 8–9
Year 4

Ages 9–10
Year 5

Ages 10–1
Year 6

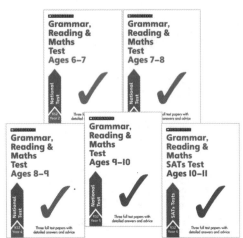

*Two full test papers are included for Maths.

"Just like the real thing"
Exam Ninja

- Boost your skills with practice papers exactly matched to the real test format

- Covers all the key test topics for Year 2 to Year 6

- Each book includes up to three full practice tests, plus answers and advice*

Revision & Practice ▸ 10-Minute Tests ▸ National Tests ▸ Catch-up & Challenge

Available everywhere books are sold

Find out more at
www.scholastic.co.uk/learn-at-home